A catalogue record for this book is available from the British Library

Published by Ladybird Books Ltd
80 Strand London WC2R 0RL
A Penguin Company

2 4 6 8 10 9 7 5 3

© Ladybird Books Ltd MMV

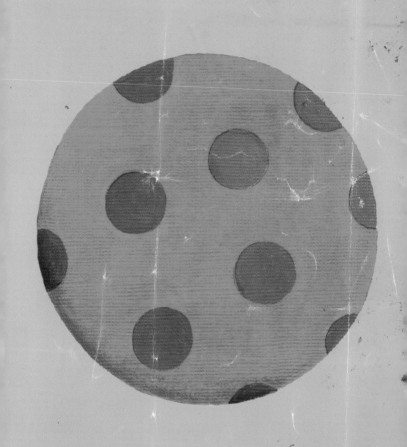

bouncy ball

noisy rattle

yellow truck

fluffy rabbit

shiny train

brown teddy

round drum

muddy tractor

Teddies and Toys

Ladybird

blue teddy

floppy doll

big car

little duck

orange teddy

spotty dog

happy lion

red bucket

pink teddy

stripy tiger

green dinosaur

spinning top

sailing boat

soft blocks

flying kite

silver robot